# ALWAYS EAT YOUR BOGIES

# ALWAYS EAT YOUR BOGIES

### And Other Rotten Rhymes

## *by*
## Andrew Collett

## Illustrated by Sue Cork

## The King's England Press
### 1998

ISBN 1 872438 20 2

Always Eat Your Bogies is typeset by The King's England
Press in Garamond 12pt and published by
The King's England Press,
21, Commercial Road, Goldthorpe,
Rotherham, South Yorkshire, S63 9BL
First published 1998, Reprinted 1998.
© Andrew Collett 1998
Illustrations © Sue Cork 1998

Printed and bound in Great Britain by

Woolnough Bookbinding
Irthlingborough
Northamptonshire

# Author's Note:

## Cow Pats Rule OK!

It's official! Children love to laugh! In hundreds of schools, libraries and shopping centres around the country I have been putting this theory to the test. In nine out of ten cases, children would rather burst into giggles than sit quietly in a corner. The evidence is overwhelming. The facts are inescapable. Cow pats rule OK!

In this collection I have brought together those poems which have always got the greatest giggles. The ditties which sent children the dottiest! The wildest, wackiest, rib-tickling riot of poetry ever. Remember - children love to laugh. It's official! So come and join me in this crazy collection of poetry.

The aim of Always Eat Your Bogies is to promote the reading of poetry through humour. Some might argue that cow pats and bogies should not be the subject of "real" poetry. I understand that. But if, through reading this book, I can establish the reading habit with just one child, then it will have served its purpose. So, happy reading!

*Andrew Collett*

Andrew's fiction and poetry is already widely published by Oxford University Press, Macmillan, Scholastic, Wayland, Ginn and Company, Evans, Playhouse Cassettes, The Early Learning Centre, Stanley Thornes, Hodder and Heinemann.

# Always Eat Your Bogies

Always eat your bogies
don't wipe them on your clothes,
just gulp them down in one
as you pick them from your nose.

For they're full of crunchy goodness
they're best when green and long,
so always eat your bogies
and you'll grow up big and strong.

# There's Nothing Quite Like A Cowpat!

There's nothing quite like a cowpat,
they're so easy to spot,
some are cold and crunchy
and others steaming hot.

Some will smell of foulsome things
like sick or sweaty feet,
whilst others will whiff of daffodils
and seem good enough to eat.

Some will look like doughnut rings
without the jam inside,
some will make you slip and fall
and others will make you slide.

Some will sit all alone
some will line in pairs,
some will be completely bald
and others might have hairs.

Some will have a smiley face
some even have a name,
for when it comes to cowpats
then no two are quite the same!

# The Everlasting Nappy.

One thing would make me happy
a super, everlasting nappy,
one which didn't get dirty or torn,
was made to measure from when you're born.

One which emptied in the night
with buttons to push to keep it white,
one with rockets down the side
to take you on a nappy ride.

So come on people everywhere,
throw your trousers in the air
tie a nappy to your bottom,
fitted once it's then forgotten!

# The Spotted Grumble Bug

Living up every teacher's nose
curled up nice and snug,
lives an amazing creature:
The Spotted Grumble Bug!

It's there to make your teacher cross
it's there to make him cruel,
for all teachers have the bug
whenever they're at school.

So, if you see your teacher twitch,
if his anger really shows,
remember, it's just the Grumble Bug,
picking at his nose!

# Please Remember Your Sink Creature

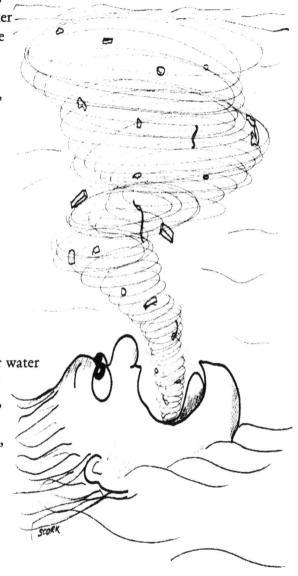

That gurgle which comes
from your dirty sink water
is the sound of a creature
gurgling one quarter,
of all of the odd things
that you flush out to sea,
like toenails and earwax
and yesterday's tea.

Like odd bits of onion
and chips out the pan
a corn flake, a peanut
spaghetti and flan,
potato with peel
all mashed into one
fish fingers, all soggy,
and quite underdone.

So please do remember
when you flush out your water
the monster who gurgles
no less than one quarter,
of all of the things
that you flush out to sea,
like toenails and earwax
and yesterday's tea.

# Grandad's Nose

Grandad likes to wipe his nose
just about everywhere,
from the carpets to the curtains
to the bottom of his chair.

He's blown bits down the telephone
he's wiped it on the floor,
he's sneezed across our Sunday lunch
like he's never sneezed before.

He's coughed and cleared his nostrils
all over Dad's new coat,
he's left green bits on the banister
from the bottom  of his throat.

He's snuffled and he's sniffed
he's shot showers in the air,
for when it comes to Grandad's nose
he wipes it everywhere.

# How To Make Belly-Burn Spread

Pour in a pimple, squeezed freshly today,
with two maggots still juicy and fat,
then drop in some dandruff, fluffy and light,
from the hair of a flea-covered rat.

Then bring to the boil, for ten minutes or more,
adding two toenails to make it a treat,
then stir in a sock, going green down below,
from the smelliest of dirty great feet.

Flick in a fingernail, drip in some dung,
dice up the dead skin from your toes,
before whisking it up with a dozen wasp wings
and the dribble from a dog's nose.

Then serve it all with blisters and boils
and bluebottles which haven't been fed,
and, after a mouthful, you'll soon work out why
they call this best belly-burn spread!

# Bite At A Blister

Bite at a blister
tug with your teeth,
get at the gunge
bubbling beneath.

Gobble it down,
leaving no waste,
for the bigger the blister
the better the taste!

# A Dungfly's Delight

The dungfly delights
in soaring to great heights,
especially when small and still young.

But what it likes best
is to bang on its chest
and dip in some freshly laid dung!

# Spot Rap

Take a spot
squeeze a spot,
squash it till
it hurts.

Take a spot
squeeze a spot,
squash it till
it squirts.

Take a spot
squeeze a spot
let it shoot
up high.

Take a spot
squeeze a spot
into your
friend's eye.

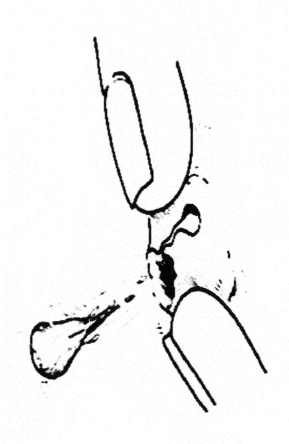

# Currant Bun Riddle

Dead flies are collected
by spiders and things,
who chew up their bodies
and crunch at their wings.

Before spitting them out
in bundles of black
to sell them to bakers
for ten pence a pack.

So next time you buy
a big currant bun,
remember the hard work
put into each one.

# The Old And Crusty Loo

All toilets grow old and grey
just like me and you,
it's not difficult to spot
an old and crusty loo.

Its lid will be on its last legs
with whiskers round its rim,
and you won't have to look too far
to spot its wrinkly skin.

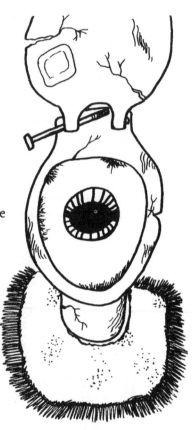

Its battered broken handle
will complain if pulled too quick,
and you'll always have to flush it twice
for old bones can sometimes stick.

Its false teeth can quickly nip
from deep inside the pan,
so if you have to pay a trip
go quickly if you can.

For all toilets grow old and grey
just like me and you,
it's not difficult to spot
an old and crusty loo.

# Our Compost Heap

Our dirty washing pile
is like a compost heap,
full of gunge and grime
and creatures crawling deep.

There are tissues stuck  together
and breeches with no bottom,
there are tights turning green
and girdles going rotten.

There are bloomers and panties
pumping out a pong,
for our dirty washing pile
has been standing for too long.

# Mary's Hooter

Mary Booster had a hooter
the shape of a giant-sized
pea shooter.
So every time she tried to sneeze
out shot a pile
of mushy peas.

# Underneath Dad's Armchair

Underneath Dad's armchair
where the vacuum never goes,
you'll find fingernail scrapings
and gremlins from his nose.

You'll find tissues stuck together
and biscuits with green skin,
you'll find wavy bits of toenail
and whiskers from his chin.

You'll find dried-up spots and pimples
and pickings from his teeth,
you'll find earwax and tummy fluff
all lurking down beneath.

For under our dad's armchair
there before your eyes,
you'll find a foul and filthy world
which grows each day in size.

# Nasty Pets

Deep deep down
where nobody goes,
in teachers' shoes
between their toes.

You'll find blue beetles
and a worm,
you'll find fat fleas
which like to squirm.

You'll find a maggot
and a snail,
gobbling bits
of old toenail.

You'll find all these,
sucking sweet,
for teachers never
wash their feet.

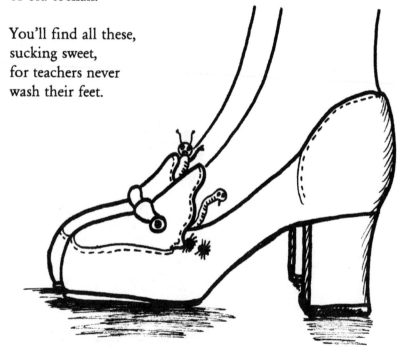

# The Planet Pong

The planet pong is where all smells
are mixed and made to stink,
from the whiff of wasted water
to the belch of blocked-up sink.

From the succulent scent of sweaty socks
to armpits never clean,
from the glow of dirty underwear
to cheese with bits of green.

From bad breath and toilet seats
from fish left out too long,
there isn't a smell in all our world
which wasn't mixed on planet pong.

# Hug A Bug

Insects aren't ugly,
that's what we say,
but are really good looking
in a funny sort of way.

So next time you spot
a dirty great bug,
just look into its eyes
and give it a hug!

# Arthur Wrigglesbottom

My name is Arthur Wrigglesbottom
I like to suck my toes,
they're the best I've ever had,
but you should try my nose.

My fingernails, another matter,
they taste of cheese and greasy batter,
but on days like this, when all's not nice,
I peel off a crispy, mouth-watering slice.

And across we go to my ear no less
where, to be sure, you'll find a mess,
for buried inside, where no one can see
is my old bubble gum to chew after tea.

And shall we go further, right up to my hair,
where in it you'll find creatures quite rare,
ones which are spotted and pull funny faces,
swing from my nose and run relay races.

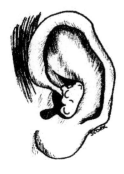

Slipping down quickly, right to my knees,
you'll find two fat blisters, and in them two fleas,
their names are Queen Sharon and King Nicholas Snitch,
between them they offer a right royal-sized itch.

And inside we go, onto my tongue,
where you'll find earwigs, particularly young,
sucking at food left firm in my teeth,
yesterday's fish and last Sunday's roast beef.

Then finally, one last trip, onto my chin
where on it live bluebottles incredibly thin,
for here they'll tell you there's so little food,
except what slips out once the earwigs have chewed.

# The Little Old Lady From 54

A little old lady from 54
dropped her handbag on the floor,
when out jumped something twice her size;
a giant spider with large green eyes.

'Oh!' She shouted, not pleased at all,
thinking all spiders should be small.
'Do go away, don't bother me!'
But the spider's thoughts had turned to tea.

But not the things that you might eat;
a plate of chips, a piece of meat,
for spiders all have one small wish:
to taste old ladies from their dish.

And rising up its eyes turned red
with flashing lights above its head,
it licked its lips, about to chew,
for of little old ladies it had had a few.

But this little old lady from 54
had seen this sort of thing before,
and waving handbag at the lights
out shot a pair of plastic tights.

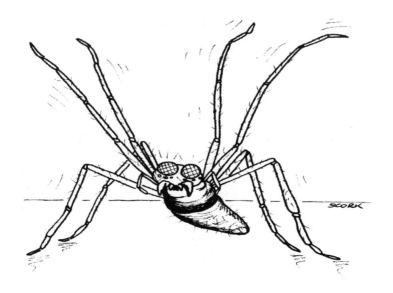

And before the spider could start to bite
the little old lady began to fight,
tying knots all round its toes,
she tripped it up then bashed its nose.

And as she lay there on the ground
she tied those tights round and round
until our spider, twice her size,
the one with great big horrible eyes
was all tied-up, every bit,
for all little old ladies just love to knit.

Which is a lesson for spiders tall,
don't mess with ladies very small,
especially those who live next door,
little old ladies from 54.

# The Chewing Gum Rule

Chewing gum left under table tops
or stuck beneath a chair,
has been put there on purpose
for everyone to share.

So don't be greedy, don't eat it all,
don't keep it to yourself,
just lick it, chew it, then pass it on
to somebody else!

# There's A Spider On Our Toilet

There's a spider on our toilet
Mum says it's big and long,
she says she'll never go again
until that spider's gone.

She says she'll run away
she says she'll never eat
until that spider, big and long,
has finished on her seat.

# Cheesy Brothers

Cheeseburgers and cheesecakes
are all my brothers eat,
perhaps that's the reason
they've all got cheesy feet!

# One Dollop Or Two

The cook in our school is a boxer
we know this is perfectly true,
for  she asks when serving our custard
if we'd like one wallop or two!

# The Vicar's Outside Loo

On every second Sunday
the church bells always ring
and the choir of St Cuthbert's
soon begin to sing.
But, not from in the church,
lined up two-by-two
another place, nearby:
the vicar's outside loo!

They start with a chant
there follows a little hymn,
this always gives the latecomers
time to squash right in.
For outside there's a crowd
always quite a rush,
to hear St Cuthbert's choir sing
and  the vicar's toilet flush!

Trebles at the front,
choir boys stretching tall,
there's nowhere else to find a space
unless you're very small.
Some do slide right under
and bounce up to the rim,
but sometimes bounce one jump too many,
flip and fall straight in.

At halftime all goes silent
all eyes on Ronnie Beat,
the choirmaster of St Cuthbert's;
King of Toilet Seat.
His one hand grabs the chain,
the other for the tap,
wriggling round the wooden lid,
it's called St Cuthbert's rap.

He jumps up in the air
and starts to sing and drone,
shouting into the toilet handle
he calls a microphone.
He sings of all the people
of those he'd like to thank;
St Cuthbert's knitting circle
for cleaning out the tank.

But not forgetting Mrs Fisher
who likes to help a lot
by keeping tulips fresh
in the bottom of the pot.
And St Cuthbert's United
as they scored their winning goal,
but mostly for their teamwork
when they change the toilet roll.

Another hymn is sung
song sheets back in place,
Doreen from the betting shop
dries her double bass.
They scrub their hands together,
as each of them will know
that Ronnie checks for dirty hands
before he lets them go.

And at the end there's a cheer
as they start to clamber out
they'll meet again in two weeks' time,
there's never any doubt.
It's down the Dog and Duck
to quench their mighty thirst,
and let the vicar back inside
before he's fit to burst.

# Our Egg Teacher

Our teacher laid an egg
and then she laid two more,
by morning play she'd managed
to lay another four.

By lunchtime she'd already
laid a dozen in her chair,
by half-past two we'd all enough
for everyone to share.

At three o'clock she stopped
as the headmaster marched right in,
glaring at our eggy teacher
and tickling at his chin.

Before stamping with his foot
and hopping on a shelf,
to flap both his feathered wings
and lay an egg himself.

# What A Team!

It's not their fancy footwork
it's not their certain skill,
it's not the way they kick the ball
which gives us such a thrill.

It's not their famous players
it's not the way they score,
it's our team's new outside loo
which makes the crowd all roar.

It's the football on the seat
to help pass the time of day,
it's the little potty underneath
for when they play away.

It's the way the toilet flushes
when someone scores a goal,
it's the name of every player
on every toilet roll.

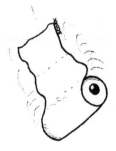

It's the whistle on the wall
to blow when you're inside,
it's our team's new outside loo
that makes their winning side.

# The School For Big Bluebottles

At the school for big bluebottles
there's no time to rest,
as these juicy fat creatures
are put through each test.

Of just how to be horrible
of how to be bad,
before being let out in the world
to drive us all mad.

They have to camp in a cow pat
for two days and a bit,
then trample fresh food
with dollops of spit.

They have to dress-up in jackets
and real combat gear,
to learn how to buzz
deep down in your ear.

They're taught how to dive
when the swatter comes out,
they're taught how to fight
if there's a spider about.

They're taught how to attack
and turn up full throttle,
so keep out of the way
of the annoying bluebottle.

# The Horror Headlice

In our school the headlice
are not tiny in size,
they don't hide in your hair
in miniature disguise.

But are as tall as the teachers
with tails to the floor,
and bulging blue bodies
which wouldn't fit through a door.
They take it in turns,
with eyes flashing red,
to choose a small boy
and suck at his head.

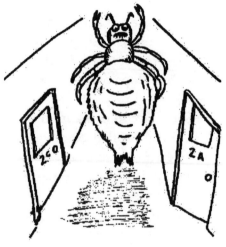

They gorge and they gobble,
for there's plenty to eat,
before burping and grunting
and falling asleep.
And as the small boy
takes a low bow,
he knows that the worst
is over for now.

At least, until tomorrow,
when the horror head lice
will be back again
for another new slice.
To gorge and to gobble
to suck and to scrape,
for from the horror head lice
you cannot escape.

# Mixed-Up Aunty

When our aunty fell into a concrete mixer
we couldn't find her at all,
in fact, no one's seen our aunty
since a new statue walked into our hall.

# Basher Jones

Outside the staff room every night
Basher Jones waits for a fight.

For Basher's nasty, Basher's cool,
Basher's the toughest teacher in school.

He roars on his bike into the yard,
for Basher's tough, Basher's hard.

He picks on the teachers and calls them names,
bashing books and spoiling games.

He makes them cry, he pulls their hair
so if Basher's about you'd better beware!

# Lord and Lady Belly Popper

Lord and Lady Belly Popper
had a daughter, quite a whopper.

Twice the size of you or me,
taller than the tallest tree.

Longer than a London bus
bigger than the best of us.

For Lord and Lady Belly Popper
with their daughter, quite a whopper.

Never stopped to take a break
from gobbling gravy or crunching cake.

From dropping doughnuts on their chin
and licking liquorice very thin.

From chewing jelly in the street,
the Belly Poppers loved to eat.

Until one day there came a sound,
the noise of cakes all sloshing round.

The din of doughnuts in a flap
and  something big about to snap.

The gush of gravy bubbling up
and something big about to POP!

For Lord and Lady Belly Popper
with their daughter, quite a whopper.

In all their lives when crunching cake
had never stopped to take a break.

Had never thought for long enough
to let their systems do their stuff.

Had never tried to stop and think
about their tummies, big and pink.

Which is why, with a slurp,
there was heard a loud and unpleasant burp.

A belch so bold it made men shake
fresh with the smell of chewed-up cake.

But a burp was not the end of this
for, all at once, there came a hiss.

A gurgling groan of blocked-up sink
coming from their tummies pink.

And then it happened, a tearing sound,
as, one by one, they left the ground.

Three belly poppers in a race
shooting high up into space.

And so the moral of this tale
is, when eating food, you must not fail.

To take a rest or have a break
from gobbling gravy and crunching cake.

So learn your lesson, fear the worst,
or one day you could also BURST!

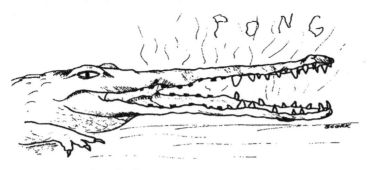

# Henry Quick

Young Henry Quick the crocodile
had a long and nasty smile,
which is normal for crocs who crawl
even  those still very small.

But Henry Quick had twice the jaw
of any croc you've seen before,
with teeth that ran right down his tongue
to crunch to bits the very young.

Except, of course, there was a catch
with teeth so far back down his hatch
he could only clean those at the front
the back ones soon went black and blunt.

Now, this isn't a problem for you and me,
we've all heard of dentistry,
but crocs with long and nasty smiles
can make your dentist run for miles.

For, with that mouth so very long,
with rotten teeth you get a pong
a smell so bad when he tried to eat
out came the whiff of smelly feet.

A stink so strong it made trees die
and sent clouds racing through the sky,
a stench to melt the cliffs of Dover
and make the smelliest pig turn over.

And so every time he sat down to dine
his tea would scarper just in time,
warned away by the whiff
of something not so nice to sniff.

Which brings me to the saddest bit
about our Croc, Henry Quick,
without some food to fill his jaw
young Henry Quick was soon no more.

# Dad's Beard

In my dad's beard
you'll find old bits of jam
you'll find mouldy milkshake
and dried-up dead ham.

You'll find lickings of liquorice
and suckings of stew,
you'll find dribbles of doughnut
and porridge like glue.

You'll find mince pie with maggots
and rancid roast beef,
for Dad dribbles his food
since he lost his teeth.

# Double The Fun!

Brothers and sisters
the message is clear,
be nice to each other
for just one day a year.

For twenty four hours
be sweetness and light,
smile at each other
and try not to fight.

Share all your things
and play with each other,
enjoy being together
as sister and brother.

Then after a break
when this day is done,
your fighting and arguing
will seem double the fun!

# Dracula's Diet

When Dracula went on a diet
things just didn't go right,
for he couldn't seem to stop himself
from nipping out for an extra bite!

# Ignorance Rules
# (A Serious Poem)

I'm bottom in my school
in maths I never score,
in learning all my tables
my teacher says I'm poor.

My handwriting could be better
my homework's a disgrace,
in every spelling test
I'm always in last place.

But talking I am good at
and for being only nine,
for pulling splinters I'm the best
and falling out of line.

For wriggling in assembly
I'd always win first prize,
and making all the teachers laugh
even though I'm half their size.

For sharpening every pencil
I'd win the silver cup,
and for making sure the paint pots
are always filled right up.

For keeping our room tidy
I'm told that I'm a star,
so why does my report say
I'll never go very far?

# Half-Price Dad

We lost our dad in the supermarket
behind the frozen peas,
but the manager offered him back at half-price
because of his knobbly knees.

# Second Helpings

'Get out! Go away!' cried the little old lady
at the woodworm gobbling her floor.

'Oh thank you,' the worm said, 'you're really too kind,
I was hoping you'd show me the door!'

# Fragrant Five-a-Side

There's always a full house,
there's never a spare seat,
each time the toilets
turn up the heat.

For it's the new craze
it's a game for us all
watching ten toilets
playing football.

Some are soaked to the skin
as they run at a dash,
for the bigger the toilet
the better the splash.

Some tackle with ease
with their two toilet feet
whilst others head the ball
with their shiny round seat.

Some sit on their own
or flush in the middle,
some open and close
as they try hard to dribble.

Some even cheat
by scoring a goal
with that extra football
from deep in their bowl.

But one thing's for certain
one thing's for sure,
when toilets play football
the crowds always roar.

# The Santa Secret

It isn't known across the world
by any mum or dad
that, for 364 days a year,
Santa's really bad.

His bedroom's so untidy
he never eats his greens,
and underneath that big red suit
Santa very rarely cleans.

He never likes to blow his nose
and will not wipe his feet,
he doesn't use a knife and fork
when it's time to eat.

So, if you're ever told at all
that Santa won't come if you're bad,
don't believe a word of this
from any mum or dad!

# The Planet Teacher

On a planet not far from here
a planet painted green,
you can hear the quiet hum
of the teacher-making machine.

For teachers are not born
they're not like you and me,
no, teachers are made from dust
then given away for free!

They're packed in big brown boxes
and trousers that never fit,
and half a dozen odd socks
from a special odd-sock kit.

And finally they're wrapped
in coloured bits of straw,
before being dropped, on demand,
through someone's staffroom door!

# Next!

Lining up in neat rows
standing two-by-two,
we all wait in silence
in that long and winding queue.

But it's not to see a statue
or get into the park,
it's not to see a museum
or a special work of art.

No, we're all lined in rows,
standing two-by-two,
waiting on our school trip
to use the one and only loo!

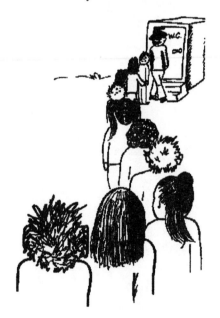

# My Pet Bear

The bear in my bedroom
is kept as a pet,
even though Dad
hasn't found it, as yet!

He does sometimes wonder
why I've started to roar,
and the reason behind
the holes in my door.

He did look quite worried
his face turned bright pink,
when the hairs from my bear
blocked-up the sink.

But he hasn't a clue
he could never guess,
the real reason behind
my room and its mess.

# Pets Are Just Like Their Owners!

Pets are just like their owners
we know this is perfectly true,
just watch a poodle with pigtails
then spot its owner's hairdo!

Watch out for lines of lovebirds
snuggling up face-to-face,
then look for ladies all weak at the knees
and staring up into space.

Even some ducks will have owners
so watch out in your street,
and if someone has a funny walk
they've probably got extra-large feet.

And finally, if you don't believe me,
then come and feast your eyes
at my sister and her hippopotamus
and the way they're both enormous in size.

# Teachers Hard At Play

Stand outside the staff room door
at any time of day
and if you listen very closely
you'll hear teachers hard at play.

For teachers don't spend their time
marking books for you,
when in the staff room
they've got better things to do.

Some make paper aeroplanes
out of homework from last week,
others disappear behind the chairs
in games of hide and seek.

Some blow long loud raspberries
at pictures of the head,
some play pin the donkey
and others just play dead.

So stand outside the staff room door
at any time of day
and if you listen very closely
you'll hear teachers hard at play.

# Our Vicar's Winning Streak

Our vicar's football crazy
he just won't be told,
that when it comes to football
then he's really much too old.

He doesn't wear a suit
just his favourite football strip,
with a cassock tucked beneath
in case his trousers slip.

He makes his congregation
sing football songs out loud,
and just before the kick-off
there's always quite a crowd.

With the bishop as the goalie
and the choir in defence,
then suddenly the game is on,
the atmosphere is tense.

A choir boy tries to pass
hymn books start to fly,
the ladies' from the knitting circle
kick the ball up high.

But the vicar's in there first
as he takes the team on whole,
dribbling with the ball
to score the game's first goal.

And as everyone starts to cheer
and jump into the air,
the vicar blows the final whistle
and says a little prayer.

# The Teacher Gang

Most teachers belong to a gang
some schools have two or three,
they meet in the teachers' toilets
after the children have gone home for tea.

They swap comics and catapults
to give them marks out of ten,
and scribble messages onto the wall like,
'must do better' and 'try this again'.

Some whisper their own special code
others do silly things for a dare,
like carving the head's name on the toilet door
and throwing their books in the air.

Then before they can all go home
before they can all disappear,
they wait for one flush of the toilet
as a signal to tell all is clear.

## Traffic Warden

At the traffic warden's grave
no one stops to pine,
on account of the meter
and double yellow line.

# Sitting On The Toilet

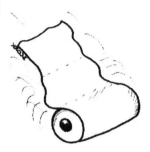

Sitting on the toilet
one finger in my ear
I wonder why Dad never put
the toilet holder near.

Near to the place
where everybody has to sit,
where Grandma picks her toes
and Mum first learned to knit.

But I can see it lurking,
that paper on the door,
two arm-lengths away
or even a little more.

Perhaps I'll stretch forward
pull myself up to the rim,
keep my feet on the floor
to stop my falling in.

Or try a dead-eyed shot
with Dad's new rubber duck
to aim right at the holder
and, with a little bit of luck,

The paper it would start
to roll across the floor,
with a second throw of underwear
would move a little more.

Then a wiggle of my foot
a pull with dirty toe,
that great roll of toilet paper
would really start to go.

Rolling for the place
where everybody has to sit,
where Grandma picks her toes
and Mum first learned to knit.

But then here lies my problem,
brings tears to my eyes,
we never buy those toilet rolls
lengthy in their size.

For as it comes much closer
right across the floor,
just before it gets to me
there's never any more!

It unravels by the bath
a last tumble on the mat,
still an arm-length away from me
and the place I'm sat.

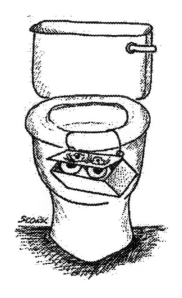

So if I could make a law,
something set in stone,
it would be that all toilets
came with paper of their own.

A handy little box
tied onto the seat,
one with pretty flowers on top
to swing beneath your feet!

# Smell Rules

Children all hide
teachers keep clear
whenever our school cook
decides to come near.

They don't answer back
or get in her way,
they lock themselves up
in classrooms every day.

But it's not that she's nasty
or terribly mean,
it's not that she likes
to make children scream.

It's not that she tries
to cast a foul spell,
it's just that our poor cook
doesn't half smell.

Of grease and fried bread
all rolled into one,
of custard gone lumpy
and meat underdone.

Of garlic with green bits
left squashed on the floor,
of that old boiled sweet
still stuck in you drawer.

Of little bits of mould
in marmalade spread,
of fingernail scrapings
left under your bed.

Of cheese with green spots
growing in size,
of milk from last week
and stale pork pies.

Which is the reason
everyone keeps clear,
whenever our school cook
tries to come near!

# Fighting Dirty!

They're round every corner
they're waiting outside,
there's nowhere to run
there's nowhere to hide.

You just can't escape
you've no chance at all,
whenever school cleaners
decide to walk tall.

They come with their buckets
and gloves pulled on tight,
they come with their mops,
ready to fight.

They come with their dusters
and sponges still wet,
to teach you a lesson
you'll never forget.

They pour out their polish
to make you run clear,
then charge with their trolleys
as they attack from the rear.

They catapult their curlers
high into the air,
before emptying their buckets
onto your hair.

They make teachers tremble
they make headmasters feel small,
whenever school cleaners
decide to walk tall.

# Waiter!

'Waiter! Waiter! There's a fly in my soup,'
cried a little old lady from behind.

'I'm sorry,' replied the waiter in haste,
'but one was all I could find!'

# Football Strip

They call me Bottomless Barrymore Blue
I'm famous around the town,
for everyone knows, when I kick a ball,
my shorts come tumbling down.

I've tried some old braces knotted with string
but it's the same if ever I score,
I feel a low rumble deep down below
As my shorts slip to the floor.

So I've an idea to help football players
Whose shorts don't seem to fit:
just wear a long jumper down to your knees
instead of your old football kit!

# Christmas Eve Trip

If you hear a creak at Christmas
in the middle of the night,
it'll just be Santa searching
to find your toilet light.

For after flying round the world
and one sherry too many,
Santa will always need to stop
and spend a little penny.

# Teacher In Love

It's happened again
he's head over heels,
he's fallen in love
he knows how it feels.

For it's not the first time
it's the second this week
our teacher in love
who won't even speak.

His eyes are glazed over
his face is one grin,
he's got little goosebumps
under his chin.

His face is a picture
as he lets out a sigh,
our teacher in love
straightening his tie.

The signs are all there
it's happened so fast,
perhaps, this time,
his new love might last.

## Rust In Peace

A man of steel rests in this spot
brave he was, they say,
now a former shadow of himself
left to rust away.

# Roar In Peace

Beware, don't come near,
this body beneath
is a man-eating tiger
who still has his teeth.

# Hot Spot!

A cook rests here in this spot
with his body still terribly hot,
for when making a curry
he was in such a hurry
that he fell right into the pot.

# Hairy Scary Insects

Why is it that insects
when ever so hairy
try to look tough
and really quite scary.

I wonder if they
might start to behave
if, once in a while,
they all had a shave.

# A Teacher's Prayer

(On the night before a school trip)

Please deliver us from children
Who can never sit still,
and spare us from small boys
who wander at will.

Please make sure our driver
might know the right way,
and could Bruiser, our bully,
be absent all day?

Please save us from swearing
and journeys too long.
Please silence all first years
if they should burst into song.

Please watch over worksheets
so they stay by my side
Please help me to cope.
Please be my guide.

And finally, one last thing,
before I fall into bed.
Couldn't another teacher
*Please* go instead?

# Our Christmas Play

Our Christmas school play didn't go very well
things just wouldn't work out at all,
one of the kings lost his way
and the crib wouldn't fit in the hall.

The angels didn't come down to earth
but found themselves stuck up a tree,
and the stable was locked for the night
for the caretaker had taken the key.

So next time we do a Christmas play
we'll try not to make it too long,
for if it's only a minute or two,
you won't notice the bits that go wrong!

# A message from the author

This collection of poetry was written by myself in response to a request for material which might encourage older children to read poetry. From cow pats to toilets it deals directly with the murky world of children's humour. As such, it may not appeal to everyone! However, to all those thousands of children around the country who have laughed with me at my many performances, thank you! For, without your laughter, I would not be able to find the courage to write at all.

# About Andrew

Andrew was a full time teacher for ten years. He now spends his time performing his material in theatres, on television and in schools. With well over one hundred individual pieces of poetry and fiction represented in a wide range of anthologies his work is never difficult to track down. His material has been published by Oxford, Macmillan, Stanley Thornes, Scholastic, Heinemann, Hodder, Wayland, Ginn, The Early Learning Centre, Evans, and others. *Always Eat Your Bogies* is his first full anthology.